This well-known fairy tale is delightfully illustrated and retold in simple words to entertain all young listeners.

Titles in Series S852

Cinderella

Three Little Pigs

Goldilocks and the Three Bears

Jack and the Beanstalk

Snow White and the Seven Dwarfs

These titles are also available as a Gift Box set.

LADYBIRD BOOKS, INC.
Lewiston, Maine 04240 U.S.A.
© LADYBIRD BOOKS LTD MCMLXXXV
Loughborough, Leicestershire, England
© Illustrations LYNN N. GRUNDY MCMLXXXV

Printed in U.S.A.

Goldilocks and the Three Bears

written by HY MURDOCK
illustrated by LYNN N. GRUNDY

Ladybird Books

Once upon a time there were three bears who lived in a house in the woods. There was Father Bear, who was huge, and Mother Bear, who was middle-sized, and Baby Bear, who was tiny. They all had their own bowls for porridge, their own chairs to sit on, and their own beds to sleep in.

One day, after Mother Bear had made
the porridge, the bears went for a walk
while the porridge was cooling.

While the bears were away, a little girl named Goldilocks came by and looked through the window into their house.

Goldilocks was a naughty little girl.
The next thing she did was to open
the door and go into the house.

There on the table were three bowls of porridge. Goldilocks tasted the porridge in the big bowl, but that was too hot. Next she tasted the porridge in the middle-sized bowl, and that was too cold. But when she tasted the porridge in the little bowl, it was just right, and Goldilocks ate it all up.

Then Goldilocks looked around the room. She saw the three chairs. When she sat in the biggest chair, she found it was too hard for her.

Next she sat in the middle-sized chair, and that was much too soft. Then she sat in the smallest chair. It felt just right. But this little chair wasn't strong enough to hold Goldilocks. It broke! Goldilocks landed with a bump on the floor.

This naughty little girl wondered what else she could find, so she decided to go upstairs. There she saw the three beds. By now she was beginning to feel tired,

so she lay down on the very big bed.
This bed was much too hard, so she tried
the middle-sized bed. That was much too
soft, so she went and lay on the smallest
bed. That was just right. Goldilocks
curled up, and soon she was fast
asleep.

By now the bears were hungry for their porridge, and they went home. But when they went inside their house they knew someone had been there.

"Someone's been eating my porridge!" said Father Bear, in his huge, gruff voice.

"Someone's been eating my porridge!" said Mother Bear, in her middle-sized voice.

"Someone's been eating my porridge, and they've eaten it all up!" cried Baby Bear in his tiny, squeaky voice.

Then they looked around the room. **"Someone's been sitting in my chair!"** said Father Bear.

"Someone's been sitting in my chair!" said Mother Bear.

"Someone's been sitting in my chair... and they've broken it!" shouted Baby Bear.

The bears decided to search the rest of
the house, so they went upstairs.
The three bears looked around.

"Someone's been lying in my bed!" roared Father Bear, in his huge, gruff voice.

"Someone's been lying in my bed!" said Mother Bear, in her middle-sized voice.

When Baby Bear looked at his bed, he cried out in his tiny, squeaky voice, **"Someone's been lying in my bed... and she's still there!"**

The sound of voices woke Goldilocks.
She sat up in bed and saw the three
bears looking at her. She was so
surprised that she jumped out of bed
and ran down the stairs, out the door,
and away into the woods, as fast as
she could go.

The three bears started to chase after her, but the naughty Goldilocks had gone. They never saw her again, and the three bears lived happily ever after.